Contents

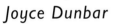

The three wishes

A poor fisherman and his wife lived in a little house by the sea. Every day the man went out in his boat to try to catch some fish for their dinner. Sometimes he was unlucky and caught nothing at all, so then he and his wife went to bed hungry.

One day the man caught a fine big fish. As he pulled it into the boat, he thought what a good dinner it would make.

Just as he was thinking this, to his great surprise the fish began to speak.

"Oh kind fisherman, listen to me,
If you will throw me back in the sea,
You and your wife may have three wishes
For I am the King of all the Fishes."

The man thought how pleased his wife would be to have three wishes, so he took the fish and threw it back into the water with a big splash.

"Thank you, fisherman," called the fish. "Now go home and make your wishes, but think carefully before you do!"

The man rowed his boat back as fast as he could, and he hurried home to tell his wife the good news.

"What good luck!" she said, when she had heard her husband's strange story. "But we must do as the King of the Fishes told you. We must sit down and think very carefully before we wish for anything."

For a long time the man and his wife talked about all the exciting things they could wish for. They could wish for a great big house to live in, or for a holiday in another country. They could wish for lots of jewels and fine clothes, or some big bags of gold. They just couldn't make up their minds. It was so hard to choose.

Now it was getting late and the fisherman was very hungry.

"Shall we have something to eat?" he asked his wife.

"We have no food," his wife answered. "You didn't bring any fish home today."

"But I'm so hungry!" said the man. "Oh, I wish I had a great big sausage to eat. That would be fine."

Suddenly, a very big sausage appeared on the table in front of the man.

"Oh, you stupid man!" his wife cried. "Look what you have done! You have wasted one of the wishes on a sausage! How could you be so silly?"

"I didn't think what I was saying," said the fisherman. "It's just that I'm so hungry! Don't blame me!"

"Well, I do blame you," his wife answered, angrily. "You are a very silly man and I wish that great big fat sausage was stuck on your silly nose so everyone could see how silly you are!"

At once, the sausage flew through the air and stuck itself on the fisherman's nose.

"Get it off! Get it off me!" he cried. He began to pull at the sausage, but it was stuck fast and couldn't be moved.

"You are even more stupid than I am," the fisherman shouted at his wife. "Now we have wasted two of our wishes and I've got this sausage stuck to my nose! Now what shall we do?"

The woman started crying.

"Oh, why did you catch the King of the Fishes?"
she said. "It wasn't such good luck after all. It hasn't
made us happy. We were much better off before. Now
we only have one wish left and we must use it to get rid
of that sausage."

So that is what they did. Then the poor fisherman and
his wife went to bed hungry once more.

The meeting of the mice

All the little house mice lived under the kitchen floor in a big white house. Outside the mouse hole, which was the door to their house, sat a fat cat, waiting.

The mice sat in their house under the floor. Old Mouse looked through the hole.

"That cat is there again," he said.

Outside the big white house, a bird was flying here and there. He flew near to the house.

"Bird, Bird, can you hear me?" said Old Mouse, from inside his mouse house.

"Yes, I hear you. I hear you, Old Mouse," said Bird.

"Will you do something for us?" said Old Mouse.

"I'll do anything I can — anything I can," said Bird.

"Will you please call a meeting of the mice? Will you ask them to meet here at our house tonight?"

"Yes, I will — yes, I will."

The bird flew away. At last he came to a corn field where some little field mice were eating corn. Bird flew down, and the field mice stopped to listen.

"All the mice must come to a meeting – to a meeting – tonight – tonight – tonight."

"And where is the meeting going to be, Bird?" said Big Field Mouse.

"Under the kitchen floor – under kitchen floor – in the big white house – big white house," said Bird, and he flew away.

Night came and the cat went to her bed to go to sleep. *Purr – purr – purr.* The field mice ran into the big house, and through the hole into the mouse house. They all sat down together.

"There is a fat cat that sits outside our door every day," said Old Mouse.

"We know," said Middle Field Mouse.

"We know because that cat sits in OUR field of corn, too," said Little Field Mouse.

"Something has to be done about that cat," said Big Field Mouse.

"That is exactly why I have called this meeting. We must do something," said Old Mouse.

"I know exactly what to do. We must get a bell. If we have a bell, we can put it around the cat's neck. Any old bell will do. Any bell at all," said Big Field Mouse.

"There must be a bell somewhere in this big house."

The mice went to look for a bell.

"There should be something here in the kitchen," said Big Field Mouse.

"There's nothing here. Not even a bit of corn. Not even a bit of cake. Not even any bread," said Little Field Mouse.

"The bell! The bell! Don't forget what we are looking for!" said Old Mouse.

15

Purr – purr – purr.

"What's that I hear?" asked Big Field Mouse.

"It's the cat," said Old Mouse. "When we hear her purr, we know she's asleep in her bed. Maybe there is something in these boxes."

So the mice looked through the boxes.

"Here's something!" said Small Mouse. "See what I have found. Listen." He rang a very little bell.

"A little bell," said Big Field Mouse. "That's a bell for a cat. It's exactly what we want."

Purr – purr – purr.

"Hurry – hurry!" said Big Field Mouse. They went through the hole and into the mouse house. They all sat down together.

"I have been thinking. This is a great thing!" said Small Mouse.

"Yes! Now we have a bell for the cat," said Middle Field Mouse.

"May I say something?" said Small Mouse. He rang the bell softly. "Please, may I ask something?"

"Ask anything you wish," said Old Mouse.

"WHO will put the bell on the cat?" asked Small Mouse.

"Not I!" said Big Field Mouse

"Not I!" said Middle Field Mouse

"Not I! " said Little Field Mouse

"Not I!" said all the House Mice.

"It makes me frightened even to think about it," said Small Mouse.

"Then we can do nothing," said Old Mouse. He rang the bell softly. "Yes, it's easy to think of an idea. But to do it – well, that's not so easy – it's not easy at all!"

All the mice nodded, and because it was nearly morning, the field mice hurried back to their field of corn, while the little house mice sat very still and listened for the cat.

Mice

I think mice
Are rather nice.

Their tails are long,
Their faces are small,
They haven't any
Chins at all.
Their ears are pink,
Their teeth are white,
They run about
The house at night.
They nibble things
They shouldn't touch
And no one seems
To like them much.

But I think mice
Are nice.

Rose Fyleman

Sun May and the dragon

Long ago, there was a small village. The people of the village were very proud because their village had been asked to make the Dragon Puppet for a big parade in the city. There was just one small problem.

No one knew what a dragon looked like!

The people went to the chief of the village and said,
"How shall we make the Dragon Puppet, oh Chief?
We don't know what a dragon looks like."

The chief was worried. It would bring great shame on
the village if they could not make the Dragon Puppet for
the parade. But he didn't know what a dragon looked
like either. What would they do?

Now the chief had three sons who were strong, brave men. When they heard of their father's problem they said,

"Don't worry, father. We will find out what a dragon looks like."

The chief's daughter, Sun May, also wanted to help.

"Never!" shouted the brothers. "The mountains are no place for a girl!"

But the chief was a wise man, and he knew that although his sons were very strong, Sun May was very clever, and so he said,

"No. Sun May must go too." So the next day, Sun May and her brothers set off into the mountains.

Before long they found the dragon's cave.

"Wait here," said Number One Son, "while I go and see what the dragon looks like." And he walked into the cave.

Like most caves, the dragon's cave was very dark, and Number One Son couldn't see a thing. He hadn't gone far when he bumped into something. It was old and leathery and it moved when he touched it.

"It feels like the wing of a bat," he thought.

Before he could say or do anything, the dragon roared. The roar was louder than the engine of a car and it made the floor shake.

The other brothers and Sun May heard the roar, and they saw Number One Son run out of the cave as fast as a rocket, back down the mountain.

"It seems the dragon has frightened our brother away," said Number Two Son. "Wait here while I go and see what it looks like." And he walked into the cave.

It was dark, and Number Two Son couldn't see a thing. He hadn't gone far when he bumped into something. It was long and scaly.

"It feels like a snake," he thought. But before he could say or do anything, the dragon roared. This roar was louder than a train and it made the cave shake.

Well, Number Two Son came out of the cave even faster than his brother. As he ran down the mountain, Number Three Son said,

"It seems the dragon has frightened our brother away. Wait here while I go and see what it looks like." And he walked into the cave.

It was dark, and Number Three Son couldn't see a thing. He hadn't gone far when he bumped into something. It was long and very sharp.

"It feels like the claw of a lion," he thought. But before he could say or do anything, the dragon roared. This roar was even louder than an aeroplane and it made the mountain shake.

Well, Number Three Son came out of the cave even faster than his brothers. Sun May watched him go and thought,

"It seems the dragon has frightened my brothers away. I will just have to go and see what the dragon looks like for myself." And she walked into the cave.

Now, Sun May was a very clever little girl. She lit a torch before she walked into the cave, so it wasn't dark and she didn't bump into anything. The dragon looked at the little girl and it didn't roar. It just looked at her.

Sun May was very frightened but she didn't run away.

"Hello," she said to the dragon. "You frightened away my brothers."

"They were sneaking around in my house," said the dragon. "What would you have done?"

"They needed your help," said Sun May. "Our village is in trouble, and only you can help us."

The dragon laughed. "Well, then, why don't you sit down and tell me all about it?" it said. So Sun May told the dragon all about the puppet for the parade, and how no one knew what a dragon looked like.

"Well," the dragon said, "We can't have that. Hop on my back and hold on. We'll be back in your village in no time."

By this time the three brothers had got back to the village. Of course, they didn't say that they had run away.

"I saw the dragon," said Number One Son. "It looked just like a bat."

"No!" said Number Two Son. "I saw it, and it looked just like a snake."

"No!" said Number Three Son. " I saw it and it looked just like a lion." And the three brothers began to fight.

Just then, the dragon flew over the village.

"Stop!" cried Sun May. The brothers looked up in surprise.

"You are all wrong about the dragon," said Sun May, "But in a way you are all right. You see, the dragon is a little like all the things you said, but each of you only saw a little part of it."

She showed the brothers which part of the dragon they had each touched: the leathery wings, the scaly tail and the sharp claws. The chief was very proud of Sun May.

"Well done, little daughter," he said. "Now, let's make the puppet."

And so with the help of the dragon and Sun May, the
village finished the dragon puppet in time for the parade.
Many people came from all over the country and they
said it was the best dragon puppet they had ever seen.

The leprechaun

One fine day a cowman called Tom was walking along when he heard a strange noise: tic-tac, tic-tac, tic-tac.

Tom stopped to listen. This time, he heard a song:

"Sing and stitch

Sing and stitch

A pot of gold

To make you rich."

Tom looked through the long grass and saw a very strange sight – a titchy-witchy man with a titchy-witchy hammer making some titchy-witchy shoes. He was a leprechaun!

Leprechauns are the clever little Irish elves who make all the shoes for the fairies. Tom knew that it was good luck to see one because if you asked, they had to take you to a buried pot of gold.

Tom didn't like looking after the cows and he thought
how good it would be to have a pot of gold and do
nothing all day. But Tom had to be very clever, for
leprechauns have a trick they like to play. If you look
away even for a second, a leprechaun disappears! So
Tom watched the little leprechaun, never taking his eyes
off him, as a cat will watch a mouse.

"Good day to you, my fine friend," said Tom.

"Good day to you," answered the leprechaun.

"How's the work?" asked Tom.

"Look after your own work," answered the
leprechaun. "Your cows are running all over the corn
field and eating the corn."

Tom was about to look round but just in time he
remembered: never take your eyes off a leprechaun!

He got hold of the little man. "Take me to a buried
pot of gold or I will feed you to my cows," he said.

"Oh, please don't do that," said the leprechaun. "I'll
take you to a pot of gold." So off they went. Tom held
on to the leprechaun as they went across the fields.

At last they came to a great big field of thistles. The leprechaun pointed to a big thistle and said,

"Dig down under that thistle and you'll find a pot of gold buried there."

The ground was very hard and Tom needed a spade. But if he went home to get one, how would he know which thistle was which when he came back?

Then he had an idea. He took off one of his bright red
socks and put it on the thistle. "Promise me that you will
not take that red sock off the thistle and I will let you
go," said Tom.

"I promise," said the leprechaun.
Tom knew that a leprechaun had to keep a promise so
he let the leprechaun go and went running home to get a
spade. Then he went back to the field of thistles.

But what did he find?

Every thistle in the field had a bright red sock on it, just like Tom's own! Tom ran from thistle to thistle, but he couldn't dig under them all.

So Tom went home, very unhappy. He never became rich and he never saw a leprechaun again, although he always listened out for the song:

Sing and stitch

Sing and stitch

A pot of gold

To make you rich.